# GRAND PRIX RACES

by **Anabel Dean**
Teacher
Redding, California

**BENEFIC PRESS**
**Westchester, Illinois**

# RACING WHEELS SERIES

Hot Rod

Motorcycle Scramble

Destruction Derby

Motorcycle Racer

Drag Race

Baja 500

Stock Car Race

Safari Rally

Road Race

Le Mans Race

Indy 500

Grand Prix Races

Library of Congress
Number 75-18274
ISBN 8175-2711-7

Copyright 1976 by Benefic Press
All Rights Reserved
Printed in the United States of America

# CONTENTS

**Chapter**

# 1

## The Formula I Car

Woody Woods couldn't believe his eyes when he walked into the House Racing Shop. There sat a Formula I car in the middle of the showroom floor.

Woody had worked on many racing cars since coming to work for Mr. House. But this was the first time he had seen a Formula I car in the shop.

"How do you like it, Woody?" asked Ann House. Her father owned the racing shop where Woody and his friend Jeff Brown worked after school and on Saturdays. She worked there, too. "It was delivered about an hour ago," continued Ann. "Whose car is it, Dad?" she asked as Mr. House came into the shop this morning.

"Spot Tate had me order that car," said Mr. House looking it over.

"You mean Spotswood Chandler Tate III?" asked Woody as he eyed the new car. "Why, he is one of the top racers in the country."

Just then Jeff walked in. As if drawn by a magnet, he walked over to the sleek car. "Where did you get that?" he asked.

"Help me roll the car out in back," said Mr. House. "I want to test it before I turn it over to Tate. It would be too noisy in here with that engine going."

Woody and Jeff helped Mr. House roll the Formula I out in back and filled it up with fuel. Then Mr. House took the cover off the engine.

"You get in and start it, Woody," said Mr. House. "I don't think I would fit into that cockpit."

Woody was very happy to have a chance to slide in behind the wheel of a Formula I car. The tight cockpit had been built for a smaller man. It fitted him like his old pair of jeans. Once Woody was in, he was lying almost on his back with the small wheel and controls right in front of him.

Then Mr. House signaled to Woody to start the engine. Woody pressed the starter and there was a broooooommmmm, broooommmmm, brooomm, and the engine died. Woody tried the starter again, and this time the sound was deafening to everyone.

Mr. House bent over the engine. Now and then he motioned to Woody to give it more gas or to slow it down. At last, he motioned for him to turn the engine off. The silence after the noise was startling.

"That engine sounds good," said Mr. House. "But I don't want it to go out of my shop until it has been road tested. You, Jeff, and Ann can take the car out to the race course and test it for me. Warm it up slowly, Woody, and then try it at high speed just long enough so that you know it is running all right. Remember that you will be driving an expensive car, so be careful."

As they loaded the race car onto Mr. House's trailer, their friend Tap came by. Tap was the drummer in the college band. As usual his drumsticks were sticking out of his back pocket. From time to time he would take them out and tap out one of the tunes he had been practicing in the band.

"Have you got room for me?" asked Tap.

"Sure, Tap. Get in," said Woody.

In a minute Tap was in the pickup with them as they headed for the racetrack. After they unloaded the car, Woody put in his ear plugs and put on his fireproof face mask and helmet. Someday Woody hoped to build his own Formula I car and race it. Today, he would get to drive one.

Woody had a Class A standing so he was licensed to drive Formula I cars, but he had never had the chance. It was his dream to get to the top step in racing someday.

He slid down into the cockpit and eased the race car slowly out onto the track. By the time Woody had gone a few laps at slow speeds, the almost lying-down position began to seem more natural. Now and then he took a quick glance at the dials in front of him. The gauges were all okay. The tachometer read 8,500 rpm. Woody shifted to second. He would take a couple of more slow laps while the car warmed up. This also gave him a chance to get used to driving on the track in the Lotus.

After two laps, Woody slowly increased the speed. He shifted to third. A quick glance at the tachometer showed 9,500 rpm. Woody listened to the engine, alert for any sign of trouble, but the car hummed along smoothly.

Woody hated to bring the car into the pits, but he knew he should. It could be years before he would get another chance to drive a Formula I car again. On the next lap, Woody brought the Lotus into the pit.

"That was some drive," said Tap.

"If this were my car, I would get some more weight off of it," said Woody to Jeff and Ann as he got out of the race car.

"I was thinking the same thing," said Jeff. "If those dual intake and exhaust valves were chromed, it would increase the airflow. I can see several ways this engine could be changed to get a few more rpm out of it."

"I see what you mean," said Ann. "And this is the latest model race car made."

"We ought to build a Formula I car for Woody to drive," said Tap. "We're due to get the rest of the money from the sale of the Beetle next month. You know we have been trying to think of a new business venture for our Woody, Ann, Jeff, and Tap Company. Why doesn't our WAJT Company build a Formula I car with our money?"

"Would you be willing to do that?" asked Woody. "My dream is to build and drive a Formula I car for the championship circuit."

"Let's get this car back to the shop now," said Ann. "Mr. Tate is going to come by to see it today. We can go someplace after work tonight and talk this over."

# 2

## Spotswood Chandler Tate III

"You're going to build a Formula I car?" asked Mr. House. "What makes you think you could build a better one than a Lotus?"

Woody and his friends had been telling Mr. House about their plan to build and race a Formula I car when they got their money for the Beetle. They had talked it over and had decided that this was what they wanted to do.

"Dad, you said the same thing when we were going to build the Beetle," said Ann. "That worked out all right. We sold it and made money."

"Okay, so that worked out. But I don't think you know what you are getting into," said Mr. House. "Why, just the body for a Formula I car would cost several thousands of dollars."

"We could do it, Mr. House," said Tap. "It'll just take a little longer."

11

Ann knew it would take her father a little while to get used to a new idea, so she changed the subject. "When is Mr. Tate coming to pick up his car?" she asked. "It has been here for four days."

"I called his house today," said Mr. House. "He will be in this afternoon."

There was a sound of squealing tires and screeching brakes from out in front of the shop. Then the front door swung open. The man standing in the doorway was wearing a pale blue jumpsuit with a bright pink scarf tied around his neck. He was wearing large sunglasses with pale blue rims. As he raised his arm to adjust his glasses, Woody saw some kind of a bracelet on his left wrist. He wondered what it was.

Everyone was so surprised to see this man in the pale blue outfit, that they hardly noticed the six men who were standing behind him, all wearing pale blue coveralls.

"I'm Spotswood Chandler Tate III," said the one with the pink scarf, glancing around the shop. "Is Mr. House here? I've come to pick up the Lotus I ordered."

"I've been expecting you, Mr. Tate," said Mr. House stepping forward. "Come with me," he said. He led the way to the back of the shop where the Formula I car was under a canvas covering.

As Mr. Tate followed, he motioned towards the men behind him. "This is my team manager, and the others are my engineers. This is my chief engineer, this is a gearbox specialist, and the others are engine and fuel and tire specialists. They will check the car over before I accept it. I have also brought my relief driver who will test drive the car," explained Mr. Tate.

"Oh, you won't need to test it," said Mr. House. "Woody Woods tested it on the racetrack last Saturday."

"I've never heard of a driver named Woody Woods," yelled Mr. Tate. "You let him drive my new car!"

"I'm Woody Woods," said Woody stepping forward. He thought maybe he could take some of the heat off Mr. House. "I have a Class A license. I only took it up to 9,500 rpm for three laps."

"No one but myself and my test driver ever drives any of my race cars. I can't accept that car. You will just have to order me another one and have it here by next Saturday."

"Mr. Tate, I can't get another one," said Mr. House. "I was lucky to get this one. There is a six-month waiting period for these racing cars. This one is okay. Why don't you have your engineers look it over before refusing it?"

The engineers gathered around Mr. Tate and began a whispered conference. They were evidently trying to talk him into letting them look at the car. At last he shrugged his shoulders and said, "My men want to look it over. But that doesn't mean we will take it."

Mr. Tate's engineers began to inspect the car. Woody, Ann, Tap, Jeff, and Mr. House all stood around watching. They had never seen anything like this before.

"My engineers want to take the car out to the racetrack for a test drive," said Mr. Tate.

The engineers rolled the race car out and onto the trailer. They got into the specially built eight-passenger van. The trailer and van were painted light blue with pink lettering, SPOTSWOOD CHANDLER TATE III, Champion Formula I Race Car Driver. Woody, Ann, Jeff, and Tap stood in the doorway watching until the van and trailer were out of sight.

Several hours later Mr. Tate's engineers returned with the Lotus. Mr. Tate had decided to keep it, but wanted it repainted in a light blue color with pink lettering.

# 3

## The Formula I

"Isn't that pretty, Woody?" asked Ann several days later. Ann had painted the Lotus a pale blue. In bright pink paint, she painted a big five on the side and the front of the car. Number five was Mr. Tate's standing in the World Championship.

"It's pretty, all right," said Woody. "But why is he having it painted blue and pink? The United States colors for these cars are blue and white."

"I guess Spotswood Chandler Tate III just wants to be different," said Ann.

"Wow!" said Jeff as he stuck his head in the door. "Mr. Tate must be afraid someone won't know he is on the track. Are you through now? We've got to go looking for a Formula I car body again if we are ever to build ourselves a race car."

Woody, Ann, Jeff, and Tap had already been out several times looking for an old racing car body and engine to buy. They hoped to find a body that had been wrecked and a Cosworth-Ford V8 engine. Today, they would go out to look again when they got through working.

Two weeks later they were still looking for a body and engine they could afford. The WAJT Company had gotten the money for the Beetle. The money would be used to buy a body and engine and to get them started racing on the Formula I circuit.

One Saturday evening they returned to the shop late. Mr. House was still working. "Guess what we have back in the shop again," he said.

"You might as well tell us, Dad," said Ann as she sat down. "We're too tired to play guessing games."

"It's Mr. Tate's Lotus. But it doesn't look the same now."

"Where is it?" asked Woody.

Mr. House just pointed to the back of the shop. There sat the twisted, bent body of the Lotus car.

"Boy, what a smashup," said Tap as he got a good look at the race car.

"What happened, Mr. House?" asked Jeff, walking around the wrecked car.

"The great Mr. Tate lost it on a corner the first time he raced the car and wrapped it around a tree. He wants me to give him an estimate for the repairs."

Woody whistled. "The whole car is going to have to be rebuilt."

When they went down to the shop after school the next day, there were Mr. Tate and his crew talking to Mr. House. Mr. Tate didn't seem to be very happy.

"I won't pay it," he was saying. "I'll buy a new car before I'll pay that much to have this one repaired."

"I know it's a lot of money," said Mr. House. "But the whole car will have to be rebuilt, including the engine. The work will take a couple of months."

"I have to have that car ready to race by Saturday," said Mr. Tate.

"No shop could have that car repaired by next Saturday," said Mr. House. "It will take a long time to do the job right. You will just have to race one of your other cars," he said.

Mr. Tate's crew of engineers gathered around him to talk. Then Mr. Tate said, "My chief engineer agrees that this car can't be fixed up to race by next Saturday. If it can't be done, then I don't want it. I'll get a new race car."

"Okay," said Mr. House.

Woody glanced at Ann, Tap, and Jeff. They all seemed to know what he was thinking. He stepped forward and said, "How much do you want for the car? We might be interested in buying it."

Mr. Tate turned around and looked at Woody. "Look, kid, you drove a Formula I car once. Now you think you are a race car driver. Well, it takes a lot more experience than that to make it on the Formula I circuit. Forget it. The price of that car is $25,000."

"We can't pay that much," said Woody. "And it isn't worth that much the way it is. We'll give you $5,000 for it."

Mr. Tate and his crew started to walk out of the shop. "Take your car with you," called Mr. House. "If you don't want me to fix it up, you will have to move it. It is taking up room in my shop."

"I'm leaving for Mexico City on Friday," Mr. Tate said. "I don't have time to fool with that car. Okay, you kids can have it for $5,000, but you won't be able to get it to run again."

"We'll bring the money out to your house tomorrow," said Ann, who was the treasurer.

"Okay," said Mr. Tate. "When I get the money, I'll give you the papers for the car." Then he walked out.

# 4

## The Scarab

The WAJT Company finally had a Formula I car. After six months of hard work and after spending thousands of dollars to rebuild the Lotus car, it was ready to be tested on the racetrack.

Ann was painting it a metallic blue color which reflected every ray of light.

"That color is so much better than the pale blue Mr. Tate used," said Woody as he watched Ann work. "We will try the car out on the racetrack next Saturday when your paint job is finished."

"What are we going to name it?" asked Ann. "All the other cars you have driven have been named after insects. But I can't think of one name."

"How does Scarab sound to you?" asked Woody. "A Scarab is this color."

"Scarab!" said Jeff. "Hm-m. Yes, I like the name Scarab."

"So do I," said Tap.

Ann opened up the can of white paint. She painted SCARAB on each side and WOODY WOODS underneath it.

Saturday morning they loaded the Scarab onto Mr. House's trailer and towed it out to the racetrack. Mr. House went along to watch the first test drive.

After they backed the Scarab off the trailer, Woody put in his ear plugs. Then he put on his flameproof face mask with his helmet over it. The goggles and gloves went on last. Woody eased himself down into the snug-fitting cockpit and fastened the safety harness.

Woody started the engine and slowly drove the car onto the track. He had been around this oval track so many times he didn't have to think about driving it. He thought only about the car and the way it handled. It was handling well and was steady on the turns. But the suspension system wasn't right.

After five slow laps, Woody brought the Scarab back into the pits. Jeff took out the spark plugs and checked them. Mr. House talked to Woody about the suspension system. They made some adjustments.

Woody took the car out for more testing.

All afternoon they worked, testing the car and making adjustments. By night they thought everything was running just right.

During the months they had been working on the Scarab, they had plenty of time to talk about future plans. They agreed to keep the WAJT Company going. By entering the Grand Prix circuit, they hoped to interest people in buying Formula I racing cars like the Scarab. Then the WAJT Company would be in the race car business, building custom Formula I race cars.

Mr. House had decided to go along as their team manager. "We have to get another engine," he said. "If we blow an engine, we would just be out of the races. But with a spare engine, we would still be in business."

They all agreed to get another Cosworth-Ford engine and fix it up. Woody would have to get more practice racing with the Scarab before the Grand Prix circuit. It was going to be a very busy summer.

# South Africa

When Woody drove into the pits and cut the engine, Ann waited for Woody to get his helmet off and to take the ear plugs out.

"You made that last lap in 1:31," said Ann as Woody got out of the Scarab.

Jeff, Tap, Woody, and Ann were at a racetrack on Saturday afternoon practicing with the Scarab. They had been paying to practice on different racetracks for the last few months.

"I think you are fast enough for the Grand Prix races now," said Jeff.

"I hope so, we have to leave for South Africa in a week," said Woody.

A week later the WAJT Company and Mr. House were flying to South Africa. The Scarab was being shipped by air. Their destination was Johannesburg.

26

The next morning after arriving in Johannesburg, they were on their way to the Kyalami racetrack outside the city. It was one of the newest and safest on the Grand Prix circuit. The country was flat with very few trees to block the view. As soon as Woody saw it, he was glad this was where he would be making his first race on the circuit.

They took the Scarab to their place in the pits and began to check it over. Woody would have only four days to practice before the qualifying race.

"Well, let's get to work," said Mr. House. "We have a lot to do."

Woody got into the cockpit and started the Scarab's engine. The powerful noise of the engine filled the pit. He cut five laps just trying to get the feel of the track. Occasionally, another race car zoomed by him. Then Woody brought the car in for another check.

For the next three days, Woody practiced on the racetrack. Slowly, he brought his speed up as he became accustomed to the Kyalami racetrack. At 6:00 p.m. on the last practice day, Woody brought the Scarab in off the track. Tomorrow he would try to qualify. His time would have to be good since there were only five places open. But could he do it?

As they all walked out of the pits together, they came face to face with Mr. Tate and his crew of engineers. Mr. Tate looked at Mr. House and then at Woody.

"Why, it's that green kid that tried to drive my Lotus," he said. "Are you following me?"

"I'm racing here," said Woody. "I will try to qualify for the race tomorrow."

"You qualify for a Formula I race?" asked Mr. Tate. "Look, kid, you'll get eaten alive out there. Those drivers are tough." Then he walked off.

Woody was worried enough. He didn't need Mr. Tate's remarks on the night before his qualifying run. Woody would just have to put them out of his mind and get a good night's sleep. Tomorrow was the big day.

# 6

## *Round I*

"We're in! We're in!" shouted Ann House as the announcer gave the names of the qualifiers. The last name heard was Woody Woods with a time of 1:29.2.

Ann was standing in the pit area with Woody and the other Scarab team members listening to the announcer. Woody was excited. He would be starting in the last row on the outside. But at least he was in the race. Mr. Tate would be in the first row in the pole position.

"He must be a great racer," thought Woody as he got ready for bed that night. He had trouble sleeping because he was thinking about his first Formula I race tomorrow. When Woody woke up in the morning, he could hear a sound. He jumped up and looked outside. It was raining.

As Woody and his crew drove out to the racetrack that morning, they could see a huge bank of black clouds off to the west. This didn't make the Scarab racing team feel any better.

There was a brisk wind and the flags and banners were crackling at the track. The crew debated whether or not to switch to rain tires. Wet weather tires would slow the Scarab down but would give more traction on a wet track. This would give Woody a better chance to stay in the race.

Woody paced up and down as he waited for the start of the race. "Let's give the car one last check," he said about an hour before race time.

"Woody, that car has been checked over and over," said Ann.

"I know," said Woody. "But for some reason I think we should check it again."

Woody got into the Scarab and started the engine. It didn't sound quite right. Woody glanced at the gauges and was startled to see that the fuel pressure gauge was low.

They had less than an hour to put on a new fuel pump. The crew worked fast and had the job done in twenty minutes. Then Woody checked the car again. The sound of the powerful engine told Woody that it was working just right.

As it got close to starting time, the rain stopped and the sun came out. But the same bank of clouds still loomed in the west. The people in the grandstand were prepared for rainy weather.

The Scarab pit crew was still debating whether or not to change to wet weather tires. About fifteen minutes before the race, Mr. House said, "Let's go for rain tires. If it does rain, the car could spin and crash. Then we would just have to pack up and go back home."

The crew worked swiftly. Other crews were doing the same thing. Some teams decided to stay with dry weather tires.

It was time to push the cars out onto the track and line them up according to their qualifying times. Spotswood Tate had the best position in the front row. Woody had the worst position in the last row on the outside.

Woody slid down behind the wheel, adjusted his goggles, and got ready. Then the flag came down. They were off! Spotswood Tate roared out in front. One glance told Woody that Mr. Tate was one of the few drivers with dry weather tires.

The Scarab felt good, and Woody began to pass a few drivers. After ten laps Woody began to take each corner just a little faster than he did before.

31

CRASH! BANG! The noise over the roar of engines startled Woody. A flash of lightning lit up the sky. Then the rain came in torrents.

Before one lap had passed, the yellow flag was out because of two separate spin-outs. The race was stopped.

All the cars returned to the pits to wait for the rain to let up. This was good for drivers and crews with problems. An hour later, the race was started again. Fifteen minutes later, it began to rain again, but not as heavily. The remaining cars in the race began to slip and slide around. On the nineteenth lap, a spinning Ferrari knocked Woody into the rail. The right rear wheel collapsed as Woody hit. He was out of his first Formula I race.

Woody watched the rest of the race from the pits. Mr. Tate won and had nine points toward the World Championship.

"Spotswood Tate is some racer," said Mr. House.

"You said it," said Woody. "After seeing the way he dresses and acts, I didn't really think he was a good driver. But he deserved that win. The way he handled that car on a slippery track without rain tires is something I'll never forget. He was the only one to finish the race without them."

# 7

## Grand Prix—Spain

"You mean practice doesn't start until five o'clock?" asked Woody as they looked at the schedule at the Grand Prix course in Barcelona. "Why do they start so late?"

"Practice is always closed during siesta time," said the race official. "The racing cars would keep the people awake. There will be a morning practice tomorrow from ten to twelve and at 5:00 p.m."

The Scarab racing team had just arrived in Barcelona that morning from South Africa. It was 1:00 p.m. and they would have to wait four hours until the course would open for practice.

Woody and his friends left to do some sightseeing in Barcelona. Time passed quickly. Soon the Scarab team was on its way back to the course for practice.

Most of the race would be on public streets. These were closed to traffic for the race and for practice.

Woody took the Scarab out and slowly brought up his speed. By the day of the qualifying runs Woody had still had very little chance to practice.

"Let's try to qualify early," said Mr. House as Woody walked into the pit area. "This track has long straights and few turns so you should make good time."

After a few warm-up laps, Woody raised his hand as he passed the timer to show he was ready to be timed.

Woody cut three laps — each one a little faster than the one before. The Scarab hugged the corners so well and accelerated so fast, that Woody's confidence returned.

The entire Scarab team gathered around him when he drove into the pits. "You made that last lap in 1:26," said Ann. "I know we're in the race."

When Woody looked up, he saw Spotswood Tate standing alone in his pit, watching the Scarab team and Woody. His expression puzzled Woody. Then Mr. Tate walked away.

The weather for the Spanish Grand Prix was beautiful the next morning. The shady streets were crowded with people who had come to watch the race.

As Woody rolled out the Scarab, he saw Mr. Tate in his light blue Matra in the first row. Woody wasn't as nervous as he had been at the start of his first race at the South African Grand Prix.

When the flag dropped, Woody roared off with the first few cars. He made a good start. After two laps, there were only five cars in front of him. One was Mr. Tate's Matra, and Woody got behind him.

The streets were wide and there was lots of room to pass. But the corners were not banked so the drivers had to straighten them by cutting across them.

Woody began to cut the corners just a little closer each time. The grandstand and people were just a blur as Woody zoomed past them. At this speed the road seemed to get narrower. When he went by the pits, Mr. House was holding up a blackboard. But the sun flashed on it, and Woody couldn't read what it said.

The tires screamed as Woody cut down low and overtook the Matra as it drifted to the outside. Woody had passed the great Mr. Tate. Now he had to try very hard to stay in the lead. Sometimes the Matra pulled even with the Lotus, but the Scarab had better cornering ability and Woody always managed to pull ahead.

When Woody passed the pits this time, he took another look. There was a big number three on the blackboard. Woody was third in a Grand Prix race.

Lap after lap went on with the Matra and the Lotus fighting it out for third. Then Woody glanced at his dials. He had lost his oil pressure. Maybe the gauge was wrong. But Woody knew he couldn't take the chance of blowing the engine. On the next lap he drove into the pits.

In a two hour race there wasn't time for long repairs. Woody yelled, "Oil pressure gone!" and still sat in the car hoping that he could get back into the race.

The crew jumped into action. After a few minutes Mr. House said, "You might as well get out, Woody. This repair job will take at least a half hour. We are out of the race."

Slowly, Woody unbuckled the harness and slid out of the narrow cockpit. Woody stood in the pit again and watched the finish of another Grand Prix race. Mr. Tate came in second. This gave him six more points towards the World Championship.

# Monaco

"What a beautiful country," said Ann as the Scarab team drove along the steep hills and cliffs overlooking the Mediterranean Sea below.

They had rented a trailer and a pickup to take them to Monaco for the next Grand Prix race. It drew a larger audience and was better known than any other Grand Prix.

Woody and his friends found a small garage close to their hotel where they could keep the Scarab and work on it.

The Grand Prix was held on the public streets which were closed off to other traffic. The pits were on a busy street and could only be used while the racers were practicing or racing. They would keep the trailer and pickup to take the Scarab back and forth to the garage.

That evening the Scarab team walked the track which was less than two miles long. As they walked, they talked about cut-off points and road surfaces. The winding streets with hairpin turns were like no track Woody had even seen or driven before. The drivers would have to slow down on these turns. Then the road went downhill towards the water and around a curve. The road running along the Mediterranean was straight, and the racers could get up some speed here. But then there was a 300-foot tunnel with a bend in it. That would be difficult to drive when coming into it from the bright sunlight. He could lose time getting used to the light change.

Woody and his friends walked down to the harbor. It was filled with yachts and other ships and boats. Many of the yachts would be grandstands for their wealthy owners on race day. The race would follow the harbor and then around a turn. Race car drivers often ended up in the harbor when they failed to make the turn. There would be boats and divers ready to rescue anyone who went in on race day.

When the team got down to Gasworks Turn where the pits were located, they were getting tired. By the time they had finished walking the entire track, Woody knew it would be a difficult race.

The next morning Woody walked the track again by himself. There were so many things to cause trouble — trees, telephone poles, seawalls, hills, signs, and the harbor. Woody wanted to get everything about the track clearly in his head.

That afternoon the crew towed the Scarab down to the pits for the first practice laps. Many of the other crews were already there, checking their racing cars.

After unloading the Scarab, Woody slid down into the cockpit and started the engine. His friends hovered over the Scarab, making adjustments. Everything hummed perfectly, so Woody turned the engine off. He hoisted himself out of the tight cockpit. It would be twenty minutes until the track opened.

"I see that our friend, Spotswood Tate, is here," said Tap.

Woody glanced around and saw that a pale blue van pulling a matching trailer had stopped nearby. Mr. Tate got out and was at once surrounded by reporters and fans.

For the next several days Woody and the other drivers practiced every day. Slowly, Woody brought his speed up as he searched for the best route around each corner. After his practice laps, the crew made adjustments and changes to the engine as they tried to get more speed out of the Scarab.

The time until the qualifying rounds was getting shorter and shorter. There would be more drivers trying to get into the race, but only five places would be given out.

Spotswood Tate was out practicing almost every day, too, and didn't seem to have any trouble making good times. Woody admired the way he drove and tried to learn something by watching him.

Woody worried about whether or not he could qualify. So far his fastest time was far too slow. The Scarab team was beginning to get a little low on money. He felt he would be letting his team down if he couldn't get in this race. If they didn't win or place in a race soon, they would have to pack up and go back home.

# 9

## Too Slow

Br-r-r-r-ooom-m-m-m! Br-r-r-oom-m-m-m!

Woody went faster as he passed the start-finish line. The tachometer climbed to 10,000 rpm before he braked for the Sainte Devote Curve, barely missing the railings on the outside. Then he sped up again for a short stretch before sliding through the left-handed Massenet Curve. The crowds on the terrace at the hotel were a blur as Woody flashed by. Woody grazed the curb as he braked and guided the Scarab around Upper Mirabeau and then down to the deadly Station Turn.

For several days Woody had been working to bring up his speed. Only a powerful car could win the Grand Prix at Monaco. But that wasn't the important thing. This was the trickiest course on the circuit.

The winner would have to be one of the top drivers in the world. Woody was beginning to wonder if he could even qualify. So far his best time had been 1:39.4 which was far too slow. But on his last lap, Woody's confidence began to rise. He was almost sure he had driven faster.

Woody could hardly wait to hear what his time was when he pulled into the pit. "What did I do?" he asked as he took off his helmet and got the ear plugs out.

Ann shook her head. "That last lap was 1:35," she said.

"Are you sure?" asked Woody. "I know I was faster than that."

"We had two stopwatches on you," said Mr. House. "They both show the same time."

"That's right," said Ann. "That last lap wasn't too good."

The entire team felt letdown as they loaded the Lotus on the trailer to take it back up the hill. There was only one more day of practice before the qualifying trials would begin. At this rate, they would never qualify. Maybe they would have to pack up and go home.

That evening the Scarab team walked down by the harbor. The yachts, trimmed with colored lights, were mirrored in the water. The streets were like a carnival as crowds of people strolled along, laughing and talking.

Woody didn't feel very happy. When the others decided to go back to the hotel, he stayed at the cafe. He had problems. How could he get more time off his laps tomorrow so he could qualify? Woody's thoughts were interrupted by loud talking and laughing. He frowned as he looked around and saw that Spotswood Tate and his team had just walked into the cafe.

Woody got up, paid his bill, and walked across the road to look at the harbor. While leaning on the seawall trying to figure out a way to get a little more speed on each lap, he heard a voice behind him.

"Is the rookie going to give up and jump into the harbor?" asked the voice.

Woody turned to see Mr. Tate leaning on the seawall beside him.

"No," he said slowly. "I'm not going to jump. But I'm not going to qualify, either. I lack the experience to drive this tricky course."

"How is my old Lotus doing?" asked Mr. Tate. "By the way, Woody, who fixed up the Lotus for you?"

"My friends and I fixed it," said Woody. "It's working great. It's my driving. I can't shave enough time off my laps."

"Come to the hotel at 10:00 tomorrow," said Mr. Tate. "I'll show you something."

46

# 10

## A New Friend

"Don't go, Woody!" said Ann. "Mr. Tate doesn't like you. He may push you over a cliff or do you some other harm. He's still angry with you for test driving the Lotus before he wrecked it."

"Don't be silly," said Woody. "He wouldn't do anything like that. I didn't like Mr. Tate when I saw him back home, but he is a good driver—the best I have ever seen."

"Why does he want to see you, Woody?" asked Mr. House.

"I don't know," answered Woody. "He just said to come to his hotel at ten and he would show me something. I really think I should go and find out what he wants me to see."

"Go ahead," said Jeff. "But I'll tell you one thing, if you aren't back by eleven, I'm going to call the *gendarmes*. I don't trust Mr. Tate."

When Woody got to Mr. Tate's hotel, he found him sitting on the terrace, finishing his breakfast. The rest of the team seemed surprised to see him.

"Oh, there's our little rookie," said Mr. Tate. "Come on, I'm going to take you for a little ride."

"Take me for a ride?" asked Woody. He could remember some of the gangster movies he had seen as a kid. Someone was always being taken for a ride. "I don't know if I have time to go riding," said Woody. "There are things I should do."

"This will do you more good than practicing," said Mr. Tate as he led the way to the Ferrari. Woody got in the seat beside Mr. Tate. He didn't know what was going to happen now.

Mr. Tate took off in the Ferrari as if they were on the start-finish line of a Grand Prix race. They climbed up the narrow, crooked streets of Monte Carlo at top speed until they were high on the cliffs overlooking the Mediterranean. Mr. Tate drove along a twisting, narrow road, skirting the cliffs. Then he drove off the road to an overlook and turned off his engine. From here you could see the entire 370 acres that made up Monaco and all up and down the Mediterranean coast.

They sat there for about ten minutes. Woody began to wonder why Mr. Tate brought him up here to look at the view. Was this what Mr. Tate wanted him to see?

Woody glanced over at Mr. Tate. He was resting his left hand on the top of the steering wheel. Woody could see the bracelet that Mr. Tate always wore more clearly. On it he read DIABETIC. It was a medical alert bracelet. Was Mr. Tate a diabetic? He must be, or he wouldn't wear that bracelet. But could a diabetic be a race car driver?

Mr. Tate began to talk. "I don't really know why I brought you up here, Woody," he said. "I have been racing for twenty years. During that time I have seen four or five young drivers come up that could really be great drivers. I have fought them just as hard as I could. This is my last year of racing. I am giving it up."

"But, Mr. Tate, you are a great racer," said Woody.

"Every time I have had injuries, it has taken me longer to get over them because of my diabetes. My sight is not what it used to be. Oh, I can fake it pretty good on the eye tests because I've taken so many of them. But I'm through racing. I'm just trying to hold out and win the World Championship before I retire. I've been close but have never won."

Woody didn't know what to say. He was surprised to find that he didn't dislike Mr. Tate anymore.

"You haven't had very good luck so far in your Grand Prix races," said Mr. Tate. "And luck has a lot to do with racing. I think you have the makings of a champion driver. You just lack experience in Formula I driving. It may take you five years or it may take you ten to make it to the top. But your timing is excellent, and I think you can do it."

"Mr. Tate, at first I didn't like you because you got so angry when I tested your car," said Woody. "But I have seen that you are the best driver on the track, and I admire you. It will be a great loss, if you have to give up racing."

"You know, Woody," said Mr. Tate. "I would like to pass on all that I know about racing to someone like yourself. Do you want me to give you a few lessons on driving the Monaco track?" he asked.

"Would you really do that?" asked Woody. "If I don't improve soon, my days as a Grand Prix driver are over."

# 11

## The Driving Lesson

"On these hairpin turns, cut across about here and use the curb over there to slide you around," said Mr. Tate. "Really scrape your tires against it." Mr. Tate was driving Woody around the track slowly in his Ferrari. He was showing Woody how he drove the course.

Woody could see some of the mistakes he had been making. He could see ways to shave off a second here and there.

When they finished driving the entire track, Mr. Tate asked, "Where are you staying? I'll drop you at your hotel. It will soon be time to practice."

"Just drop me along here," said Woody. "I want to walk back to the hotel. You don't know what it means to me to have you show me how to drive," said Woody. "I don't know how to thank you, Mr. Tate."

53

"Someone helped me once years ago," said Mr. Tate. "So maybe I do know what it means. Come around to see me again if you have more questions or problems."

Then he was gone and Woody started walking up the steps to the hotel on the hill.

"It is after 12:00," said Ann when Woody walked into the hotel. The Scarab team was in the lobby, looking worried. "Where have you been?" she asked.

"Mr. Tate has been giving me a driving lesson," said Woody. "He's a great man and a good driver."

"Do you mean Spotswood Chandler Tate III?" asked Mr. House. "Are we talking about the same man?"

"Yes, we're talking about the same man," said Woody. "Come on, let's have some lunch and then get down to practice. I'm going to do a lap in less than 1:30 today."

While they ate, Woody told them all about his talk with Mr. Tate and the driving lesson. They were just as surprised as he had been.

By 2:00 p.m. the team had hauled the Scarab down to the pits and were ready for the afternoon practice. Tomorrow the cars would start qualifying for the big race.

When Woody first took the car out, he went around the track trying to remember everything that Mr. Tate had told him earlier.

Then he began to speed up a little on each lap. On the curves the Scarab scraped the curb on one side and then cut across. By sliding the back wheels into the curb on the other side, he used it to straighten out for the road ahead.

Woody thought his timing was better now. After five laps he drove into the pit to find out. "How am I doing?" he asked.

"Your last lap was 1:33.3," said Ann.

His time was better than it had been but not good enough. "I'll try it again," said Woody as he took off his helmet to wipe his face. "Maybe I can shave off a couple more seconds someplace."

Woody started out again. This time he revved the Scarab's engine up to 10,500 rpm. He raced around Sainte Devote Curve, fighting to keep from hitting the railing on the outside. He was driving close to his limit of control, but he was beginning to have more confidence. Woody drove five more laps, each time straining the Scarab to its limit.

The checkered flag came out, ending the practice for this afternoon. When Woody drove into the pit this time, everyone looked happy. He knew he had improved his timing.

"Your time was 1:31," yelled Ann.

Mr. Tate strolled over as the team was loading the Lotus onto the trailer.

"Hi, Mr. Tate," said Woody. "My timing is better, but I have some more questions to ask you about some of the turns and corners. I forgot a couple of things you told me."

"Would it help to follow me around for a few laps tomorrow?" asked Mr. Tate.

"Yes, it would," said Woody. "Thanks very much, Mr. Tate."

As the team pulled the Scarab back up the hill, the qualifying trials the next day were on everyone's mind. Could they do it?

The first day of the qualifying rounds was very hot. It looked almost like race day as the Scarab team pulled their race car down to the pits. The stands were full of people who came to watch the action. Many of the teams were working to make last minute repairs and adjustments so their cars could qualify. Woody and his friends checked over the Scarab to make sure everything was working just right.

When the track opened at 3:00, Woody drove by the Matra pits slowly. Mr. Tate waved and pulled out in front of him. Mr. Tate hadn't forgotten his promise. Woody followed the Matra around for several laps.

Some of the things Mr. Tate had been telling him became clearer as he followed the Matra. Then the Matra speeded up, and Woody tried to keep up with it.

After seven laps, the Matra went into the pits. Woody brought the Scarab in, too. There wasn't anymore time to try to qualify today. At 5:00 the checkered flag was out, and the roads were turned over to the five o'clock traffic.

For several days, while racing cars qualified, Woody practiced. He was trying to cut his lap time down a little more before trying to qualify. Then there were only two more days left. Woody would make his first qualifying run the next day. There would still be another day left to try again if necessary.

The next day the team took most of the fuel out of the car so Woody could get a little more speed. Everything went well during practice, so Woody raised his hand as he passed the timer to show that he was going to try to qualify.

Woody revved the engine and tried to do everything just a bit faster than he had before. He was getting used to the shortcuts Mr. Tate had shown him, and they were beginning to feel natural. The people and houses were just a blur as he went around corners and over dips. Around each lap, he squeezed just a little more speed out of the Scarab. When he brought the car in, he knew that his timing had been better than ever before. But, was it good enough?

"What is it?" asked Woody as he took his helmet off.

"It's 1:28.7," said Ann. "As of now we're in the race."

The next day the team was back again. Woody cut a few practice laps and they waited to see if anyone could better his time. But when the qualifying rounds closed that night, Woody was still one of the five drivers to qualify. Woody's position would be in the seventh row in the Grand Prix the next day. Spotswood Tate would be in the first row as usual.

# 12

## Grand Prix—Monaco

Woody sat up and looked at the clock. "It must be 10:00 or 11:00 o'clock," he thought. It was only 7:00 a.m. Woody lay down and looked at the cracked ceiling in his little hotel room. His friends had told him to stay in bed until 10:00 or 11:00. He would need his rest. The big race was today. The more he thought about it, the more restless he became. "I've got to get more sleep," he said aloud.

Woody was used to getting up early. He lay in bed thinking about each turn, dip, and straight of the track, and the way he should drive it. But, today, it would be different. A race wasn't the same as practice. Woody didn't think he could go back to sleep, but the next time he looked at the clock it was 9:30. He got up and dressed. Then Woody went down to the dining room.

Woody had a light breakfast. He wasn't afraid, but his stomach felt a little funny. Besides, the worst thing a driver could do was to eat a heavy meal before a race.

The time passed slowly until noon. Then Woody went up to put on the woolen underwear he wore for races and the flameproof racing clothing. The woolen underwear soaked up the sweat better than the flameproof ones. And there would be plenty of sweat today. The temperature was already at ninety. He checked to see that he had his helmet, two pairs of goggles, ear plugs, gloves, shoes, and fireproof face mask in the bag he carried with him to the pits.

Woody never wanted to talk before a race. His friends knew this and never said anything to him before a race unless they had to. They drove down to the pits in silence.

As they drove along, they could see that all the boats in the harbor were now moored farther out from shore. The only boats allowed near shore were a few small motorboats, which carried a doctor and frogmen. Woody knew they were there to rescue any racers who went into the harbor.

Trucks loaded with TV equipment were parked at the best viewing spots. The stands were filled with people, as were the hills and balconies of buildings nearby.

The flags of all the countries were blowing in the breeze. It was a colorful sight, but the Scarab team hardly noticed it. They did notice several ambulances and the hospital van parked close to the pits. The police were everywhere. They were trying to keep the track clear and the crowds back. A police officer waved the Scarab team on into the pit area with their equipment.

The pits were beginning to fill up with Formula I cars and their teams. Mechanics were making some last minute repairs and adjustments. Pit crews were getting tires, fuel, and parts laid out.

The drivers seemed to be the only ones who weren't busy. Most of them just paced up and down, mopping the sweat from their faces. Few of the drivers wanted to talk before the big race. All were uncomfortable in their flameproof clothing.

As the hands of the clock moved closer to the starting time, the teams began to test the engines. The roar of the 450 horsepower engines was deafening.

Just before the 3:00 p.m. starting time, Prince Rainier III and Princess Grace arrived. The national anthem of Monaco was played by the band. Then the Prince and Princess drove around the track to officially open it for the Grand Prix.

The tension of the drivers rose as they got into position for the race and waited for the flag to drop. Woody was in the seventh row on the inside. He could see Mr. Tate's Matra in the first row. The signal was given to start the cars. The roar of the engines sent a flock of pigeons flying into the sky.

Then the flag came down. Woody let the clutch out, and the Scarab roared off. There was a traffic jam right in front of him on the starting line. A driver had given a Brabham too much gas, and it had fishtailed around. But Woody pulled his car to the left and squeezed between the front of the Brabham and the curb. By the time he got around him, the pack was out in front.

Woody followed the pack through Sainte Devote and down the straight to Massenet Curve. There was no way the ones who started towards the back could get through. Woody had one glimpse of Mr. Tate out in front, fighting for the lead. For the first few laps Woody had no choice but to stay towards the back of the pack. But by the fifth and sixth laps, the racers were beginning to string out, and Woody could speed up. At last it looked as though he would be able to move up. Lap after lap went by, and Woody soon passed up a Brabham, a Tyrrell, a Shadow, and a McLaren.

After forty laps, only fourteen of the twenty starting cars were in the race. When Woody passed the pit this time, he saw that he was in tenth place. That sounded pretty good, but there were only fourteen cars left in the race. He had to go faster.

Woody came up behind a Cooper-Maserati. This car could pull away from the Lotus on the straights, but the Scarab could corner better. Woody followed the Cooper-Maserati for four laps before he was able to pass. But slowly he was working his way up in the pack. As he passed the pit this time, the blackboard had a big eight on it. Woody was in eighth place!

Once in a while Woody got a glimpse of Mr. Tate in the Matra. He was having a great day and had moved ahead of the second place Brabham. Woody had wondered before what he would do if he had a chance to pass Mr. Tate. He could see now that he would never catch up.

On lap 60 Woody saw a red Ferrari in his rearview mirror. This puzzled Woody. Mr. Tate's Matra and a Brabham had been fighting for first place with that red Ferrari right in back of them. How had the Ferrari gotten by them? Where were the Matra and the Brabham? On the next lap, Woody knew the answer.

The Matra and the Brabham were both out of the race on Gasworks Turn. They had evidently locked wheels and crashed into the railing. In one quick glance, Woody saw the two drivers standing beside the track. At least Mr. Tate wasn't hurt. Maybe he could get back into the race.

But Mr. Tate didn't get back into the race. When Woody went by the pits this time, he saw a six on the blackboard. Woody was in sixth place. His chances to win were getting better after each lap. But, could he keep going at this speed?

Woody pushed the Scarab harder. There were less than twenty laps left in the race. The remaining cars began to take more chances as the end of the race was in sight.

The 1,500 or more gear changes on every lap were beginning to take their toll of the racing cars. Woody was beginning to lose his second gear. He tried to avoid using it as much as possible and began to take many of the corners in third instead of second. He was often on the edge of losing control on these curves, but this was no time to hold back. Now and then he had to make corrections as he felt the car start to spin. He passed a McLaren after following it for five laps. He had gained on the Ferrari which was leading by about sixteen yards.

Time was running out. Woody was worried about his own car lasting out the race. The second gear was completely gone, and he had to take all the corners faster. It was taking all his driving skill just to keep the Lotus on the track at these speeds. When the checkered flag came down, Woody was right in back of the Ferrari and a Cooper-Maserati. Woody thought he was on the same lap, but he wasn't sure.

It took Woody a few seconds to realize the race was over. He made one slower lap, and then drove into the pits. After racing with the noise and excitement, Woody was a little dazed when he turned off his engine. The silence seemed strange.

The Scarab team was jumping up and down, but Woody couldn't make out what they were saying. He unfastened the harness and hoisted himself out of the car. A few reporters had come into the pit to talk to them. But most of them were in the big crowd gathered around the Ferrari.

When Woody got his helmet off and the ear plugs out, he could hear Ann yelling, "We're in third place! Woody, we're in third place!"

# 13

## *After The Race*

That evening the Scarab racing team had dinner at the Hotel de Paris to celebrate. Mr. Tate and his friends were there, too. It was a fun evening.

Mr. Tate came over to talk with them and to congratulate Woody on his third place win. Woody now had four points towards the world championship. Mr. Tate was still in first place with fifteen points. The Matra could be fixed, and he planned to be in the Dutch Grand Prix race in Holland.

The WAJT Company had some good news, too. The afternoon of the Monaco Grand Prix race, a group from Australia came over to talk to the Scarab team about ordering a couple of the specially-built Lotus cars. They had been watching Woody driving the Scarab during practices and for the big race.

The Australians liked the way the team built the Scarab and wanted two racing cars set up just like it. Woody and his friends were thrilled to get the orders. This business would keep the WAJT Company busy all next winter.

On the way back to their hotel that evening Woody, Jeff, Ann, Tap, and Mr. House could see the lights of Monte Carlo and the yachts in the harbor. All Monaco seemed to be celebrating the Grand Prix tonight.

"I'm sure going to be sorry to leave tomorrow," said Woody.

"Yeh," said Jeff. "This has been the best race we've been in."

"Thanks to Mr. Tate's help," said Woody.

"Well, you had something to do with it too, Woody," said Ann.

"Superior driving...and don't forget the superior help," said Tap.

They all started to laugh at Tap's little joke. Then Mr. House said, "Well, team, tomorrow we'll be off to Holland for the Dutch Grand Prix. With a bit of luck, we might come in first this time."

## History Of Grand Prix Racing

The first race to be called a Grand Prix, or Grand Prize, was organized in 1906 by the Automobile Club of France (ACF). It replaced the Gordon Bennett Cup races organized by an American, John Gordon Bennett, in Paris in 1900.

The Grand Prix of the ACF soon ranked as the world's number one speed contest. Soon, other countries were organizing their own Grand Prix races.

After World War II the name of the organization which controlled Grand Prix racing was changed to the International Automobile Federation. In French it is known as Federation Internationale de l'Automobile, or FIA.

The FIA makes and enforces the rules governing all international Grand Prix races. If a driver wants to be recognized as a world champion, he or she must race and win in events specified by the FIA. This organization is composed of delegates from all countries who are represented in Grand Prix racing.

Up until 1925, a mechanic rode in the passenger's seat with the driver in the races. Pictured at the bottom of page 70 are three race drivers and their mechanics in the Grand Prix at Lyons, France, in 1914. Pictured above is Jimmy Murphy of the United States with his mechanic in the Grand Prix race in Le Mans, France, August 9, 1921. The mechanic was needed to perform many duties during the race. After 1925, only the driver was allowed in the racing car during races.

## The Formula Cars

The International Automobile Federation (FIA) sets up the formulas for each type of formula car. The original Formula III racing car was referred to as the world's only four-wheeled motorcycle. The Cooper Formula III was designed to run on alcohol. It did not have a starter, generator, battery, headlights, bumpers, or a passenger seat. There wasn't any drive shaft, and the power was transmitted from the engine to the rear axles by chain.

Today, the Formula III is a standard racing car, powered by gasoline. Many a Formula I champion started racing by driving a Formula III car.

The Formula II cars are smaller than the Formula I racing cars. The specifications for the Formula II cars are about two-thirds of those set by the FIA for the Formula I.

The most important formula car is the Formula I. This car is the only one driven for the World Championship of Drivers in Grand Prix racing.

All Grand Prix cars are open-wheeled, or without fenders. They are single-seated and the drivers sit in a semi-reclining position.

Formula I cars have a *monocoque* body. This means that the body and frame are a single unit like a metal tube.

## STP Grand Prix Car

This is Mario Andretti's European Grand Prix mount, built near Oxford, England, by the March Engineering Group. This Formula I car was used in road racing events abroad and in the United States during 1970.

73

## Lotus Type 72

Pictured above and below is the John Player Special Lotus Type 72 Formula I car driven by Ronnie Peterson during the 1974 racing season.

# The World Championship Of Drivers

In 1949, an Italian delegate to the FIA proposed that a point system be established to give points for each Grand Prix race. He wanted a World Championship to be awarded each year to the driver who made the most points in Grand Prix racing for that year. All the delegates to the FIA approved of this plan. The first World Championship for a driver was awarded for the 1950 season.

## POINT SYSTEM FOR GRAND PRIX RACING

| Place | Points Awarded |
|---|---|
| First | 9 |
| Second | 6 |
| Third | 4 |
| Fourth | 3 |
| Fifth | 2 |
| Sixth | 1 |

The Formula I driver who places first in the World Championship of Drivers is entitled to have the number one painted on his car the following year. Other drivers may have the number of their standing in the World Championship of Drivers painted on their race cars.

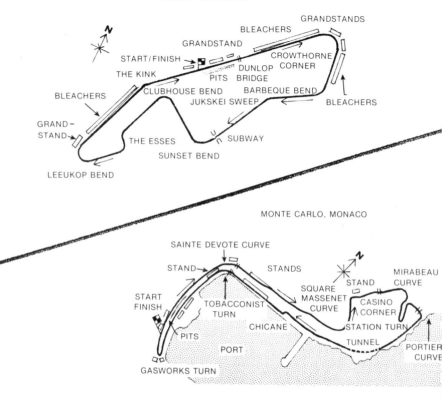

KYALAMI RACETRACK

MONTE CARLO, MONACO

## Grand Prix Racetracks

Shown above are maps of the Kyalami Racetrack outside of Johannesburg, South Africa, and the Monte Carlo, Monaco, race course for Grand Prix racing.

At first Grand Prix races were held on regular roads, which were closed to the public during races. The race at Monaco has been held on the public streets of Monte Carlo since 1929. Today, most races are run on tracks especially built for Formula racing.

The countries where the championship races are held are not always the same. From time to time one racetrack is dropped for lack of safety or some other cause. Then another track is counted in the point championship. Some countries have more than one Grand Prix track.

### Applaud The Winner

Prince Rainier and Princess Grace of Monaco applaud Jackie Stewart of Scotland, winner of the Formula I Monaco Grand Prix race on May 23, 1971. It was Stewart's second victory at Monaco.

# About The Racing Wheels Series

**Hot Rod** - Woody Woods wants more than anything to own a hot rod and enter it in the hot rod derby. Buck Brown and his friends have other plans for Woody.

**Motorcycle Scramble** - A paper route too big to handle without wheels leads Woody to become interested in motorcycles. After fixing up his motorcycle, Woody is ready to try a motorcycle scramble: a real test of how well riders can ride.

**Destruction Derby** - Woody Woods needs some money so he can buy parts to make his hot rod even faster on the track. The $300.00 prize makes the Derby a "must" for Woody.

**Motorcycle Racer** - Woody Woods finds himself in competition again with Buck Brown as he joins Mr. Sands on the summer racing circuit. Find out what happens on the track as Woody races for the finish line.

**Drag Race** - Woody's hot rod, the Bumble Bee, is fast, but not fast enough to beat Buck Brown in the Drag Races. With the help of a strange new friend, Woody makes his hot rod even faster. But is it?

**Baja 500** - The Baja 500 is the roughest off-road race there is. Woody, Jeff, Tap, and Cathy take their rebuilt jeep, the Sand Flea, to Ensenada. Together, they enter it in the race. The going is tough, but Woody and Jeff make it to the finish.

78

**The Stock Car Race** - Woody's interest in cars leads him to Mr. House's racing shop, and a chance to work on real stock cars. Woody learns something from a pretty visitor, and gets his chance to race a stock car.

**Safari Rally** - When an accident puts Jeff out of the East African Safari Rally, Ann House steps in to help Woody Woods on an adventure-filled drive through East Africa.

**Road Race** - Woody Woods, while driving a high powered Lotus in a road race, is in an accident. His hands badly burned and his leg broken, he says he will never drive again. He gets over much of his fear, but it is on the day of the big road race that he must make a big decision.

**Le Mans Race** - Woody and his friends succeed in building Woody's new invention, a flywheel car. The wish to have their pollution-free car manufactured leads them to the twenty-four-hour race at Le Mans.

**Indy 500** - The Indy 500 is the toughest test of car and driver. Few drivers who begin the race finish it. Woody Woods has something to prove to himself and to his friends: that a "road race" driver can win at Indianapolis.

**Grand Prix Races** - Woody Woods and his friends have finally built a Formula I car for Grand Prix racing. Follow Woody and his friends as they travel the Grand Prix circuit.

## Acknowledgements

Richard D. Wahl - Illustrations

Materials and photographs provided by:
  Historical Pictures Service, page 70.
  STP Corporation, page 73
  The John Player Motorsport Press Office,
    page 74
  United Press International, pages 71, 77.